The Fanatics Guid

D.I.Y.

Cartoons by Roland Fiddy

EXLEY
NEW YORK • WATFORD, UK

Other cartoon giftbooks by Roland Fiddy:
The Fanatic's Guide to Cats
The Fanatic's Guide to Computers
The Fanatic's Guide to Golf
The Fanatic's Guide to Husbands
The Fanatic's Guide to Love
The Fanatic's Guide to Sex

First published in hardback in the USA in 1996 by Exley Giftbooks
Published in Great Britain in 1996 by Exley Publications Ltd.

12   11   10   9   8   7   6   5   4   3   2   1

ISBN 1-85015-773-1

Printed in Singapore.

Exley Publications Ltd, 16 Chalk Hill, Watford, Herts, WD1 4BN, United Kingdom.
Exley Giftbooks, 232 Madison Avenue, Suite 1206, NY 10016, USA.

CASUALTY

Unfortunately, "Do-It-Yourselfers" have to…

...live with their mistakes.

"For goodness sake don't admire his fretwork – he might give us something!"

"You were lucky – the paint pot broke your fall!"

"You might as well go back to George – your father is redecorating too!"

1.

2.

Even the most efficient "Do-It-Yourselfers"…

3.

...get stuck from time to time.

"I like it, except I <u>hate</u> green!"

1.

2.

3.

4.

Whether you are decorating a living-room or tiling a bathroom,
make sure you see eye to eye with your partner.

"It's the garden shed self-assembly kit we ordered!"

"Stop asking stupid questions and call a mechanic!"

1.　　　　　　　　　**2.**

Do-It-Yourselfers should always be willing…

3.

…to listen to informed advice.

"I'm calling about the electric drill you sold my husband."

1.

1.

2.

4.

"Don't hurry me! A rushed job is a botched job."

"I'm sorry, Bert – it was either drop the can or have an accident."

1.

2.

3.

4.

"I'm ready to say to hell with it if you are!"

Teamwork is the key to successful decorating.

"Help!"

"You should go up again immediately or you'll lose your nerve!"

"I think it's your way of getting away from it all!"

1.

2.

3.

4.

"How's it going, Michelangelo?"

"No thanks – I'm just browsing."

"Well, I don't think you've read it at all!"

"His enthusiasm is infectious!"

Books in the "Crazy World" series
($6.99 £3.99 hardback)

The Crazy World of Cats (Bill Stott)
The Crazy World of Football (Bill Stott)
The Crazy World of Gardening (Bill Stott)
The Crazy World of Golf (Mike Scott)
The Crazy World of Housework (Bill Stott)
The Crazy World of Marriage (Bill Stott)
The Crazy World of Rugby (Bill Stott)
The Crazy World of Sex (Bill Stott)

Books in the "Fanatic's" series
($6.99 £3.99 hardback, also available in a larger
paperback format, $4.99, £2.99)

The Fanatic's Guides are perfect presents for
everyone with a hobby that has got out of hand.
Over fifty hilarious colour cartoons by Roland Fiddy.

The Fanatic's Guide to Cats
The Fanatic's Guide to Computers
The Fanatic's Guide to Dads
The Fanatic's Guide to D.I.Y.
The Fanatic's Guide to Golf
The Fanatic's Guide to Husbands
The Fanatic's Guide to Love
The Fanatic's Guide to Sex

Great Britain: Order these super books from
your local bookseller or from Exley Publications Ltd,
16 Chalk Hill, Watford, Herts WDI 4BN.
(Please send £1.30 to cover postage and packing
on 1 book, £2.60 on 2 or more books.)